THE SYAMANTAKA GEM

PRINCE SATRAJIT OF DWARAKA WAS A DEVOTEE OF SURYA, THE SUN GOD.

YOUR DEVOTION MERITS A GIFT. THE SYMANTAKA GEM IS YOURS. TAKE IT.

THE SUN GOD DISAPPEARED.

THE JEWEL SHINES SO BRIGHTLY THAT IT LIGHTS MY PATH.

SATRAJIT RODE BACK TO DWARAKA WEARING ABOUT HIM THE RADIANCE OF THE SYAMANTAKA.

WHAT HAS HAPPENED TO OUR PRINCE?

HE SHINES WITH A STRANGE LIGHT.

WONDERSTRUCK THEY WENT TO SHRI KRISHNA, THE ALL-KNOWING ONE.

LORD KRISHNA, BEHOLD! THE SUN HAS COME TO EARTH.

SURYA HAS GIVEN SATRAJIT THE SYAMANTAKA JEWEL.

THE JEWEL HAS THE POWER TO PREVENT FAMINE AND WAR.

MEANWHILE SATRAJIT REACHED HIS PALACE.

HAIL!

HAIL!

4

THAT NIGHT HE WENT TO BED, WEARING THE GEM.

THE NEXT MORNING—

GOLD COINS!

HE INSTALLED THE GEM IN A TEMPLE...

5

...AND WORSHIPPED IT.

IT GIVES FORTH EIGHT MEASURES OF GOLD A DAY!

THE GEM BROUGHT PEACE AND PROSPERITY IN ITS WAKE.

WE HAVE BEEN FAVOURED!

WE WILL NEVER KNOW FAMINE OR WAR!

ONE DAY KRISHNA VISITED SATRAJIT.

WELCOME, SHRI KRISHNA.

DWARAKA IS HUMMING WITH TALES OF YOUR GOOD FORTUNE

I OWE IT TO SURYA.

BUT IT IS THE FRUIT OF YOUR DEVOTION.

NOW THAT YOU HAVE ENOUGH GOLD, WHY DON'T YOU GIVE THE GEM TO KING UGRASENA?

WHY SHOULD I?

BECAUSE HE IS THE KING. THE GEM WILL BE SAFE WITH HIM.

IT WILL BE EQUALLY SAFE WITH ME. I WILL NOT PART WITH IT.

A FEW DAYS LATER, SATRAJIT'S BROTHER, PRASENA, WENT OUT ON A HUNT, WEARING THE JEWEL.

TAKE CARE, PRASENA.

I MAY LOSE MY LIFE BUT I'LL GUARD THE JEWEL.

WHEN HE REACHED THE FOREST, PRASENA DISMOUNTED AND WAITED FOR THE GAME.

AH... AT LAST.

8

A SNAKE!

WHAT A NARROW ESCAPE!

BUT—

AA AGH!

AS THE LION WALKED AWAY WITH THE GEM, JAMBAVAN, KING OF THE BEARS, SAW HIM.

WHAT A FINE JEWEL!

HE ATTACKED THE LION...

...AND KILLED IT.

I'LL GIVE IT TO MY SON.

HERE IS SOMETHING FOR YOU, SON!

MEANWHILE AT DWARAKA—

PRASENA HAS NOT RETURNED FROM THE HUNT.

WHAT COULD HAVE HAPPENED TO HIM?

I AM SURE, KRISHNA MUST HAVE KILLED MY BROTHER FOR THE SAKE OF THE GEM.

SATRAJIT SUSPECTS ME.

I MUST FIND THE JEWEL AND ESTABLISH, MY INNOCENCE.

11

A FEW HOURS LATER—

IT IS PRASENA!

HE'S DEAD! RED MARKS ROUND HIS NECK... A BROKEN BRANCH...

LOOK! LION TRACKS!

FOLLOW ME. IT LOOKS AS IF HE WAS KILLED BY A LION.

LOOK, GOLD COINS.

THE LION MUST HAVE SOMEHOW GOT HOLD OF THE SYAMANTAKA JEWEL.

AH! THERE LIES OUR CULPRIT.

I WONDER WHO TOOK THE GEM.

DEAD!

I WONDER WHO KILLED IT.

WAIT HERE. I WILL GO INTO THE CAVE.

THE GEM!

I MUST TAKE AWAY THE JEWEL WITHOUT SCARING THE CHILD.

14

16

THE WINNER TAKES THE GEM.

THEY FIRST FOUGHT WITH WEAPONS.

THEN WITH STONES AND MOUNTAIN ROCKS...

...AND WHEN THOSE WERE EXHAUSTED, WITH UPROOTED TREES.

MEANWHILE, OUTSIDE THE CAVE—

IT IS TWELVE DAYS SINCE HE WENT IN THERE.

HE MUST BE DEAD.

HE ASKED US TO WAIT HERE.

I AM HUNGRY!

I AM TIRED.

LET'S GO HOME.

AN OWL HOOTED—

WHAT WAS THAT EERIE SOUND?

ONLY AN OWL.

LET'S GO AWAY.

OVERCOME BY FEAR AND EXHAUSTION, THEY LEFT.

MEANWHILE AT DWARAKA KRISHNA'S WIFE AND PARENTS WERE ANXIOUS.

THERE IS NO NEWS OF KRISHNA.

MY LORD, RETURN TO ME, SAFE AND SOUND.

LOOK! A CLOUD OF DUST.

KRISHNA?

BUT—

WE HAVE COME BACK WITHOUT KRISHNA.

WE FEAR HE IS DEAD.

KRISHNA WAS NOT DEAD. AFTER TWENTY EIGHT DAYS OF CONTINUOUS FIGHTING—

YOU ARE INVINCIBLE. I SURRENDER.

ALONG WITH THE GEM PLEASE ACCEPT...

...MY DAUGHTER, JAMBAVATI FOR A WIFE.

I WILL, BUT SOON AFTER THE WEDDING WE MUST RETURN TO DWARAKA. I HAVE TO RESTORE THE GEM TO ITS OWNER.

NO SOONER HAD THEY GARLANDED EACH OTHER THAN JAMBAVATI TURNED INTO A BEAUTIFUL WOMAN.

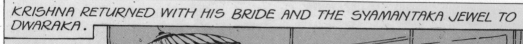

KRISHNA RETURNED WITH HIS BRIDE AND THE SYAMANTAKA JEWEL TO DWARAKA.

KRISHNA HAS COME, WITH A LOVELY BRIDE.

TELL SATRAJIT TO COME TO THE COURT. I HAVE SOMETHING FOR HIM.

WHEN SATRAJIT CAME—

I HAVE FOUND THE SYAMANTAKA GEM.

AFTER KRISHNA HAD TOLD HIS STORY—

I DID YOU GRIEVOUS WRONG.

IT WAS OUT OF YOUR IGNORANCE.

SATRAJIT WANTED TO MAKE AMENDS.

KEEP THE JEWEL, KRISHNA...

...AND ALSO ACCEPT MY DAUGHTER, SATYABHAMA IN MARRIAGE.

I WILL MARRY YOUR DAUGHTER WITH PLEASURE. THE GEM IS RIGHTFULLY YOURS. KEEP IT. YOU MAY HOWEVER GIVE ME THE GOLD IT YIELDS.

MEANWHILE, SATYABHAMA'S DISAPPOINTED SUITORS, AKRURA, KRITAVARMA AND SHATADHANWA, NURSED THOUGHTS OF REVENGE.

SHATADHANWA, WE HAVE BEEN INSULTED.

YES, SATRAJIT HAD PROMISED HIS DAUGHTER TO ONE OF US. WHY DON'T YOU KILL HIM AND MAKE THE SYAMANTAKA JEWEL YOURS?

EAGER TO POSSESS THE GEM, THE EVIL SHATADHANWA DECIDED TO KILL SATRAJIT.

THE JEWEL WILL SOON BE MINE.

A..A..AH!

TAKING THE GEM...

...SHATADHANWA RODE AWAY.

THE WOMEN OF SATRAJIT'S HOUSE, SET UP LOUD LAMENTATIONS.

SATYABHAMA WAS HEART-BROKEN.

FATHER...
FATHER...

SHE WENT TO KRISHNA WHO WAS IN HASTINAPURA.

LORD, MY FATHER HAS BEEN SLAIN.

YOU MUST BE BRAVE.

MEANWHILE THE GUILTY SHATADHANWA APPEALED TO KRITAVARMA.

PLEASE, SHELTER ME FROM THE WRATH OF KRISHNA.

GO ELSEWHERE.

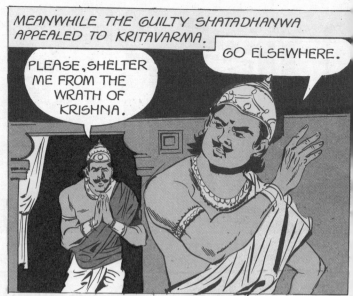

SHATADHANWA THEN WENT TO AKRURA WHO GAVE HIM THE SAME ANSWER.

AKRURA, PLEASE KEEP THE GEM WITH YOU THEN. I'M FLEEING FROM DWARAKA.

SHATADHANWA FLED. KRISHNA AND HIS BROTHER, BALARAMA WHO FOLLOWED IN HOT PURSUIT SOON CAUGHT UP WITH HIM.

HALT! YOU MURDERER.

IT'S KRISHNA. I'M DOOMED.

NEAR MITHILA, ONE OF SHATADHANWA'S HORSES TRIPPED...

...AND FELL.

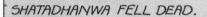

SHATADHANWA FELL DEAD.

HE DOES NOT HAVE THE JEWEL. HE MUST HAVE GIVEN IT TO AKRURA.

WHEN KRITAVARMA LEARNT OF SHATADHANWA'S FATE—

KRISHNA HAS KILLED SHATADHANWA, I HEAR.

HE WILL COME HERE NEXT. LET US FLEE BEFORE HE GETS HERE.

28

UNLESS THE GEM IS FOUND, I WILL REMAIN SUSPECT IN THE EYES OF THE PEOPLE. ONLY AKRURA CAN HELP ME. I WILL SEND FOR HIM.

WHEN AKRURA CAME —

I KNOW SHATADHANWA GAVE THE SYAMANTAKA GEM TO YOU FOR SAFE-KEEPING.

29

PERHAPS HE HAS HIS REASONS TO ACT THE WAY HE DID!

ANYWAY I WILL NOT SPECULATE IDLY. THE JEWEL IS MINE AND WITH IT, PROSPERITY.

HAVING SET THE MINDS OF THE CITIZENS AT REST KRISHNA TOO WAS ABLE TO RELAX IN THE COMPANY OF HIS MANY WIVES.

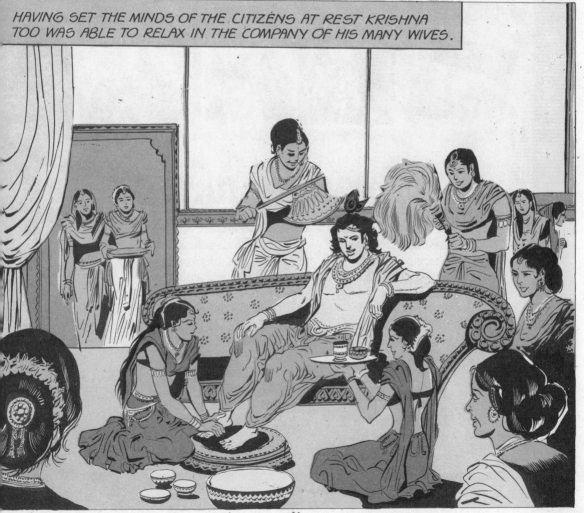